Loving
the essence of being
a butterfly in dementia care

Loving

the essence of being
a butterfly in dementia care

Sally Knocker

Consultant Trainer, Dementia Care Matters

Seventh in the **Feelings Matter Most** series

Sally Knocker has worked for twenty five years in the dementia care field. She has particular interest in meaningful activity and occupation in the broadest sense for older people. From 2002, she worked for NAPA, the National Association for Providers of Activities for Older People, initially as a project manager and then as Director of Communications. Sally has written extensively on the topic, for example the Alzheimer's Society Book of Activities (2002), Counsel and Care's Not Only Bingo (2007), a range of NAPA publications and for the 'keeping active and occupied section' of the SCIE Dementia Gateway website. Sally has run reminiscence groups with the European Reminiscence Network and an intergenerational arts project with Magic Me. Sally joined as a full-time Consultant Trainer with Dementia Care Matters in April 2012 as she wanted to join an expert team of leading edge dementia care consultants.

Dementia Care Matters is a leading UK organisation inspiring culture change in dementia care across the UK, Ireland and internationally through University Learning, Butterfly Care Home Development, Learning Resources, Tailored Training, Mattering in Hospital and Mattering At Home, alongside Dr David Sheard's own consultancy as CEO/Founder, Dementia Care Matters.

Dementia Care Matters Ltd
St Georges House
34–36 St Georges Road
Brighton
East Sussex BN2 1ED
T: 01273 242335
W: www.dementiacarematters.com
E: info@dementiacarematters.com
Twitter: DCMatters
Facebook: Dementia Care Matters

ISBN 978 1 874790 74 7
© Dementia Care Matters 2015
First published 2015 by
Hawker Publications Ltd
Culvert House
Culvert Road
London SW11 5DH
T: 020 7720 2108
W: www.careinfo.org
E: info@hawkerpublications.com

British Library Cataloguing in Publication Data.
A catalogue record for this book is available from the British Library.

Hawker Publications publishes a range of books for the health and social care sectors, with a particular emphasis on dementia care.

Editor: Dr David Sheard, CEO/Founder, Dementia Care Matters.
Printed and bound in Great Britain by Truprint Media, Margate.
Designed by Peter Francis.

Contents

Acknowledgements

Heartfelt thanks to the following people for their contributions to the production of this publication:

Butterfly Project and Butterfly Service™ homes working with Dementia Care Matters, where we have experienced many uplifting examples of people sharing the day and living life well. Many of the ideas in this book have come from homes that are embracing the 'Butterfly' approach and making it a reality moment by moment.

David Sheard, Chief Executive and Founder, Dementia Care Matters for believing that I could be the author of the 'L' in the 10-book 'Feelings Matter Most' series (with the acronym which makes up BEING ALIVE) and for his huge support and direction in shaping the book.

Gilly Brooks, Gwen Coleman, Daren Felgate, Maureen Howe, Peter Priednieks, Luke Tanner and Helen Walton, the wonderful Dementia Care Matters consultancy team who have shared the ideas that they have seen in action as they support care homes through the culture change process. They have also personally shown me many of the core essences in this book, especially 'friendship', 'sharing' and a sprinkle of much needed 'play.'

Cassie Rogers, Operations Manager and the Dementia Care Matters office team for their support in making the final draft a reality.

Anita Astle, Louise Collins, Eve Carder, Deborah Evans, Ann Gray, Ros and Rob Heath, Lesley Hobbs, Santall Horn and other inspirational managers for sharing their experiences and their photographs which tell the stories.

Peter Francis for his patience and resilience in creating countless designed drafts of the book and staying with us to the finishing line.

FrogBox Marketing for the oil essence, butterfly and 'S' factor illustrations.

Dr Richard Hawkins and Sue Benson at Hawker Publications for their belief in a book that is a bit different from other 'activity' books.

Loving, the Essence of Being a Butterfly

If you look up the word 'essence' in the Oxford Dictionary there are various definitions. The one that strikes me is:

'The intrinsic nature or indispensable quality of something which determines its character.'

The indispensable quality of really good dementia care simply must involve wanting to be loving in our approach towards people. Being loving became unfashionable in the world of 'care'. Being loving became confused and associated with vulnerable adults needing protection from inappropriate relationships. It was replaced with a so called type of 'detached professionalism' that led to distance and coldness towards people. The essence of care became institutional.

Yet it was fairly obvious that boredom, lethargy, being left staring into space or lacking a loving relationship in life is unhealthy and creates bad feelings inside people. There is now significant recognition again in care homes that people's feelings really do matter most. Responding to feelings is seen again as the true essence of being caring when this is balanced with knowing the person's wishes and needs really well.

The experience of living in a care home from here on must surely guarantee a basic human right – that each person will be reached and connected with in a loving meaningful way that feels right to the person. The essence of positive dementia care in the future has to be that we all want to connect with people as individuals. This has to be about offering and providing people with what is the essence of still feeling and BEING ALIVE.

For the last twenty years much has been written about the need in dementia care both for 'activities' but also for more meaningful occupation. There are now a wide variety of resources and publications to assist us all in ensuring that people are engaged in 'activities' that are inviting, fun and varied.

This is not another book on activities but on connecting to the essence of living. Dementia Care Matters believes that the provision of any 'activity' is only as good as its relevance to the person, their individual past life or present enjoyment. We feel that an activity's success is only likely to be achieved in relation to the manner and quality of the relationship in which it is provided. In other words it's not about just DOING 'activities' but 'BEING together' with someone.

This is why we use the idea of Being a Butterfly – as a metaphor to capture the very essence of how to create colour in people's lives.

This book sets the provision of 'activities' in the wider context of achieving the right culture of care and offers the very essence of what works – being loving. When we see people experiencing dementia care that looks, sounds and feels institutional it can be easy to be sceptical about our ability to really change dementia care once and for all – however really focusing on the essence of being loving is the key.

Time is of the essence too in dementia care. People need to feel they matter now. Ensuring great dementia care flourishes can seem complex but in essence it is simple. It is wanting to really BE with someone.

Santall Horn, a care home manager sums this up so well:

'Life is not about striving to be a success but rather about valuing the moment, it's not about having and getting – it's about giving and being.'

I hope this book helps you to grasp the very essence of Loving being a Butterfly.

Dr David Sheard

Introduction: The Essence of the Moment

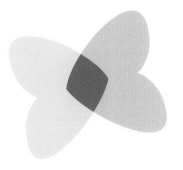

'Love is like a butterfly
As soft and gentle as a sigh
The multi-coloured moods of love are like its satin wings
Love makes your heart feel strange inside
It flutters like soft wings in flight
Love is like a butterfly, a rare and gentle thing'

Dolly Parton

When we see a butterfly in a garden, usually our spirits lift. The characteristics of a butterfly are in being unique and colourful. They are needed to pollinate flowers and thereby create beautiful gardens. Put very simply a butterfly can change the moment.

This book aims to share lots of ways in which people working in care homes can become butterflies and transform many moments. The experience of Dementia Care Matters' work in care homes over the last twenty years is that once the whole staff team learn how to be butterflies and how to connect with people, there are many fewer periods in the day where people experience loneliness and long periods of boredom. Many of the ideas shared in this book come from the homes which have worked to achieve Dementia Care Matters' Butterfly Service™ status.

Like people, no one butterfly is the same as the other. The skills in being a butterfly can be different too. In dementia care it is vital to find loving people who can be butterflies. Some will 'flit' from one person to another to create magic moments whilst other butterflies know when it is important to stay and be still with one person for a longer time.

The essence of being a butterfly is TRANSFORMING THE MOMENT.

'Do not wait for the perfect moment. Take the moment and make it perfect.'

Anonymous

The Essence of Mattering

'Mattering is a feeling deep inside that to someone or something and somewhere you really count.'

David Sheard

Most of us have a strong sense of when we matter and feel it when we don't. To matter is feeling inside that others appreciate us and that we are loved and wanted. The biggest fear for many of us as human beings is when we have a sense that no one really cares about us at all and that other people may not even notice our existence. When we sense we matter, we can cope with life's daily knocks better and know that we are not alone in the world.

Reducing feelings of boredom, loneliness and worthlessness really matters

Dementia Care Matters has conducted many hundreds of one-day observations of care homes across the UK and Ireland. What becomes very evident in observations is that, for many people living in institution-like settings, the day can feel very long with monotonous routines and a sense of care workers being busy 'doing for' rather than 'being with' people. In our findings of observations of 600 care home audits, 70% of the day was spent in what we describe as 'neutral care.' This includes people sitting doing nothing, feeling bored, sleeping because there is nothing else on offer, being cared for but with little or no meaningful interaction or engagement. It is therefore relatively easy to define what people **don't** want:

- Loneliness – little or no sense of relationship or connection with others.
- Boredom – nothing to do or to look forward to, apart from the usual events such as mealtimes and personal care.
- Lack of freedom and control over every aspect of your life.
- Worthlessness – where nothing you say or do is valued by others and where you no longer feel you have anything to give.
- Never getting outside or feeling connected to a community.
- Lack of appreciation or not being seen as an individual.

Dementia Care Matters would describe all these things as the opposite of what it means to 'matter.' The things that give us a feeling of mattering have been documented by Dementia Care Matters (Sheard 2013) and are relatively simple to describe:

Feel – knowing our feelings matter most in life.

Look – turning a place into feeling 'at home'.

Connect – feeling needed and reached.

Occupy – having a purpose and feeling busy.

Share – valuing relationships with people.

Reach – being loved for who we are.

Relax – sensing acceptance and freedom.

Matter – nurturing and looking after oneself.

Recognising that there needed to be an increased focus on people mattering, there has been a powerful movement in the health and social care sector over the last 10 years, which has focussed on dignity in care. The essence of mattering certainly involves being treated with dignity. However over the next 10 years the essence of really evidencing that people matter in dementia care homes is likely to shift in emphasis over to mattering being seen as a human right. The Equality and Human Rights Commission stated in 2014; 'Putting human rights at the heart of health and social care services can deliver better outcomes.'

Many of the other essences in this book relate back to the core essences of loving and mattering. Activities which are organised and delivered without attention to ensuring that individuals participating feel that they matter are likely to do more harm than good.

MATTERING is having evidence you can see, hear and feel that you make a difference and are needed (Sheard 2013)

2

The Essence of Identity

'When I danced, believe you me, people noticed! All eyes turned you know and there were many medals too! Would you like to see?'

Phyllis, living in a care home

There are many different ways we might describe ourselves. Some of us may think first in terms of our relationship to others; e.g. as a mother or a son. Others might see their job role as a very defining part of their identity, particularly if it is an occupation they have done for a long time. For some individuals their religious faith or their sexuality might be something which is particularly important in their lives. There are also people for whom an interest might be their biggest passion for example gardening or rugby.

Drawing on people's life and work stories, when thinking about ways to spend the day, really matters

What distinguishes an 'excellent' care home from one that is 'good'? At Dementia Care Matters, one of the key things we look for is a sense that activities are not just generalised for everyone to participate in but there is an immediate sense that individuals are occupied in a way that has particular significance to them. This often requires some 'out of the box' thinking from the team and more importantly the ability to go along with the current reality of that person. Somebody's job is what gives many of us a sense of purpose and a structure to our day. There are therefore a lot of ways to engage individuals which connect with their previous occupation.

The following are some real examples of the way people's past lives are maintained in care homes they are living in:

The matron of a care home
'If an incident happens she will complete her own paperwork. We all at some point have faced a disciplinary with her. Being part of the team has helped her settle.'

The pub landlady
'We give her a piece of paper and she writes out the menu for us. When you say certain food, she will tell you if it is a good seller or not!'

The window cleaner

'We leave out the bucket, chamois leather and sponge and he will often just get on with cleaning the windows.'

The decorator

'We fill an empty varnish tin with water and he spends many happy hours painting the light pine railings in the garden. The wood darkens each time he puts the water on it and he is very meticulous about "cutting in".'

The miner

'He will spend periods of the day under the stairs moving soft play blocks around. He likes crawling low on the floor as he works. He has a hard hat with a headlight, a tool belt and a snack box and we will give him a call for his tea breaks. There is a telephone booth in the corridor so he can call for his own taxi.'

The librarian

'We collect damaged books and she will spend many hours re-gluing and mending damaged book spines. She also likes sorting the books in various categories.'

The fire fighter

'He will check all the fire exits and help with fire drills. He knows the exact location of all the fire extinguishers.'

The secretary

'We have installed a telephone in her room and the nurses will ring her throughout the day. She is meticulous about taking messages on her pad. If you dictate a letter to her, she still writes extremely fast shorthand.'

What are important to note about these examples are the things that people have done to enable the person to feel busy and useful; 'We give her a piece of paper…', 'We leave out the bucket…' 'We have installed a telephone…'

Quite understandably there are some people who will not want to carry on working and let you know in no uncertain terms as the following example illustrates:

The Cook

'We try to encourage Gladys, who was a cook in a care home, to share her recipes and even cook but she remembers that she has retired so she laughs and tells us to "get lost" as she's "had her years of working"!'.

Many of the ways in which people prefer to be occupied relate to personal aspects of their IDENTITY and connect with their life and/or work history

The Essence of Sharing

'It's amazing what a reaction I get from people when I show a photograph of my dog or tell a silly story about what my daughter got up to at school today.'

Annie, working in the laundry

One of the things which brings pleasure and meaning to our day is the sense of being in relationship with others. Even watching a television programme or going to the shops has a different 'feel' when we are sharing the experience. If we are walking or driving with someone, we will notice the things that we see together and talk about them. If someone tells us about an experience they have had, it will often trigger a memory of something similar in our own lives. If we have something that is worrying us, the 'problem shared' is often less stressful.

Supporting the whole team to be themselves and share more of their own lives at work really matters

It is obvious that the most important resources of all in a care setting are the life experiences, personal qualities and diversity of its care workers. However it is surprisingly rare to find a care home that really encourages individuals to not only draw on this day to day but to see this as a valuable way to create connections between people working and living together. When team members talk about coming to work to be part of a family and there is a sense of love between people living and working in a care home, then it is evident that genuine sharing is happening.

Bringing out the best in people

Przemek, a young Polish worker, is vacuuming the lounge one afternoon when an art activity is happening at the table. He looks interested in what is going on and the Activity Co-ordinator asks him if he likes art. Przemek comes to the table and starts to sketch a portrait of one of the women sitting at the table. He is clearly an accomplished artist and several people in the group become very engaged watching him at work. A proper easel is purchased, future portrait sessions are organised and become a very popular activity in the home not just for those who are being painted but for those who are watching too.

19

The following are simple ideas for the team to bring into work and share – these have worked well in Dementia Care Matter's Butterfly Service homes:

- Wedding photographs or personal albums to share with people.
- Pet or animal pictures – or, better still, bringing in a friendly pet for a visit.
- Baby or children visits or photographs to show.
- 'Guess the baby' competition with photographs of staff as children.
- Motorbike or a car to admire or to help wash.
- Costumes – drama or dance and giving a performance.
- Making cakes or things to sell at a School fair.
- Asking advice relating to something personal e.g. 'Do you think it is better to send my daughter to an all-girls secondary school or a mixed school?' 'What do you think I could give my husband for his birthday next week?'
- Themed days related to the cultural backgrounds of care workers in the home where the team dress up in traditional clothes and bring in food, music or other objects related to the country they are from.

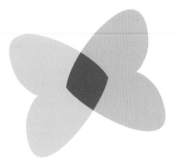

Using what you wear to create Butterfly moments

One of the reasons Dementia Care Matters Butterfly Service homes do not support care workers being in uniforms is that individual clothes create lots of great opportunities to 'change the moment.' People who are happy to maximise this will wear lots of bright colours, T-shirts with fun messages to read, hats or hair accessories which catch the eye, different coloured shoes etc. Patterns with flowers, butterflies or birds or elements of sparkle in the design will also catch the eye. This is a very visible and tangible way of sharing yourself at work. It is amazing what a transformative impact this can have within a home, as people living with a dementia will notice and respond to the vibrancy and diversity of people's dress. Care workers from other parts of the world may bring particularly beautiful colours and textures in traditional clothes.

The most important thing in creating a loving relationship is to SHARE ourselves

4

The Essence of an Experience

'It Ain't **What** You Do – It's **the Way** That You Do It…'

Bananarama

> We all have things to do in our daily lives that don't necessarily give us any particular pleasure. These are often linked to routines and things which are not very interesting. In contrast, if we have an 'experience', it is something which we can really get involved in and get satisfaction from. However, it is possible for us to change a routine task into something enjoyable by either changing the way we think about it, or possibly doing it in a different way.

Knowing how to transform an everyday task into an enjoyable experience really matters

There are many tasks in the day in care homes that can be changed into an experience, from having a bath, serving tea or eating lunch.

A good start to the day

When Anna supports Gladys to get up in the morning, she knows that Gladys likes a small drink of fresh orange juice when she wakes up. She also loves a warm flannel to wash her face and wake her up a bit. Gladys likes the curtains to be opened just slightly and for Anna to say a little bit about what the weather is like outside. Anna asks Gladys if she would like to listen to the Radio and will turn it on to her favourite channel. She will then come back about half an hour later to check whether Gladys feels ready to 'get up and go!' yet. Anna will often have a little chat about what has been happening with her family at home that morning which Gladys enjoys. When choosing what to wear, Anna will bring out one or two dresses or trousers and they talk about colours and how warm a day it is. Gladys loves to wear jewellery and also enjoys other accessories such as scarves and hats. When she puts on her watch, she likes to talk to Anna about her oldest brother who gave her the watch for her fortieth birthday. She has a variety of lipstick colours and she enjoys choosing which one to wear for the day. Gladys can brush her own hair but Anna will sometimes help style it in a particular way.

In this example it is clear that Anna has made the most of lots of elements of the 'task' of 'getting up and dressed' into connecting with what is important to Gladys – sharing and having a chat and reminiscing about families, making choices and feeling good about her appearance which has always been important to her.

Every part of the day from the moment someone wakes up in the morning to when they go to bed at night can be turned into a positive EXPERIENCE

5

The Essence of Usefulness

'I'm looking back to the life I used to lead. I used to be a person doing and now I'm the receiving. It takes a lot of getting used to you know.'

Gwyneth, living in a care home

Most of us feel good about ourselves when we are able to do something for others. This might be something practical or emotional, but it gives us a sense of feeling busy and purposeful and that we still have a valuable contribution to make. Throughout our lives we have many opportunities to feel useful as partners, parents, sons and daughters, friends and through our work roles. Our confidence and self-esteem is increased even in small moments when we feel we 'make a difference'.

Finding ways to support people to carry on feeling useful really matters

If you ask many older people there is a sense that they experience an ongoing feeling that they are not as 'useful' any more. People have spent busy lives looking after others in their families and/or their work roles. The transition to always 'receiving' and not 'giving' can be a very difficult one and it is possible to continue to help people to feel useful.

Leading the way

'I said to Evelyn I was going to the toilet. She asked me if I knew where the toilet was and whether she could show me. She took me along the hallway to the toilet, turned on the light for me and waited outside for me to come out. This was one of those moments when you know you are in a care home which is supporting people to still give as well as receive. Evelyn clearly had such a sense of wellbeing inside that she still felt able to help other people. I felt really cared for and Evelyn felt happy that she had been able to help a friend.'

What can care workers do to help people feel that they are still 'givers'?

There are many simple examples of this:

- Asking a person to help wash or brush your hair.
- Taking turns to paint each other's nails.
- Reading to a visiting child.
- Feeding or walking a pet.
- Writing or sending a birthday card to a relative.
- Carrying on a work-related or domestic activity.
- Contributing to the life of the care home in other ways.

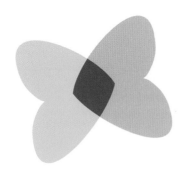

Wedding advice

A care worker approaches three women who are seated sharing a cup of tea together. She tells them that she needs their help – she is struggling to decide which dress to wear for a forthcoming wedding. She lifts a dress from her bag and shakes it, holding it up to show the women whose eyes are wide and they all comment in their own way how lovely it is – looking to each other to gauge opinion. The care worker tells them she will try it on and be back in a minute. The women have been given some anticipation and they look to each other and smile.

She returns wearing the dress and asks the women what they think – she prompts, asking their opinion of the colour and if it suits her and the women respond with expressions of enthusiasm and interest. After a few moments of discussion the care worker sits down telling them that she is also unsure which perfume to wear and really would like them to help her choose. One by one she removes three different perfumes from her bag and hands them to each in turn – they sniff and comment. After several sniffs, the debate becomes serious and the care worker presses them for an opinion; which do they like the best? Which is suitable for a wedding? Each woman takes one last sniff, offers an opinion and the decision is made. The care worker expresses how grateful she is for their help – that she feels better now and will enjoy the wedding and bring some photographs to share with them.

Creating the right invitation matters

If you ask anyone 'Would you like to do the washing up?', the majority of us are likely to reply 'no!'

Care workers might say that people don't want to do things, but there are different ways of engaging people's interest:

- **Start the activity yourself**; put a washing bowl out on a table and start to wash up – hand someone the tea towel and say 'Would you be able to give me a hand with drying these up?', 'I need your help', or using a bit of playful humour; 'I'll wash, you dry?'

- **Give a person a sense that their participation is valued** and important to you; 'I would like to invite you to join me for a dance…'

- **Find out what might be the 'carrot'** for an individual – for one person it might be being invited to do something by a handsome man, for another it might be the appeal of a glass of wine!

- **Show not tell** – Use fewer words and more physical demonstration of what's being offered e.g. if you are inviting someone to come into the garden, bring a flower to show someone, if you are doing some cooking, put some bowls, recipes, spoons, etc. out on the table to give clear visual indicators what is happening.

Many people want to carry on being USEFUL – giving as well as receiving

6

The Essence of Being 'At Home'

'Be it ever so humble... there's no place like home...'

John Howard Payne

The definition of 'home' may have different qualities for us all but for most it represents feeling safe and secure in an environment which is familiar. For some people it is the objects that surround us that help us feel anchored and comforted, whereas for others it has nothing to do with material items and more to do with the love that we feel and the relationships we share. Most of us like being truly able to be ourselves at home: we can do what we want when we want. It might be relatively little things like going to the fridge to get something to eat or turning on a radio to a channel that we prefer. 'Home' for many of us is a place where we feel free and in control.

Creating a sense of people feeling at home inside themselves matters

The key to this essence is getting to know what home means to each individual and not just home as a building or an address but home as a **feeling inside**.

These are some of the important elements to consider:

- Paying attention to and respecting each person's unique rituals and rhythms in the day – are they an 'owl' (a late night person) or a 'lark' (an early bird)? – What's personally important for them about dress, food and familiar routines?

- Knowing people's favourite places – lying with feet up on a sofa, sitting by a window, walking in the garden, relaxing in own bedroom.

- Finding the right mix of time alone and in company – a sense of peace and space, feeling amongst friends and family, being with babies and children or pets.

- Nurturing the 'freedom to be' – for people to wear what they want, to find a snack and eat when they want, to go outside when they want.

Top Tip

Talk to each person and their families or friends about what were the important things for them about being at home – think about the ways in which you might be able to re-create some of those elements in the care home.

~

- Valuing key objects – books, photographs, a favourite piece of jewellery, a telephone or a preferred mug for tea.

- Involving people in jobs they might have done at home such as cleaning windows, drawing the curtains at night, fetching milk from the fridge.

The sense of freedom and control is a vital element and particularly being able to go outside. New design of care homes is helping in this area, but it is critical to do everything to try and avoid people feeling that they are trapped in a building.

Household activities create many opportunities for enjoyable experiences throughout the day

In order to make a care home feel more like a house, an accessible kitchen area is an essential element of home. The sights and sounds of a kitchen can give people a real sense of involvement in home life.

Meals are one of the main 'tasks' of the day in care homes yet they can potentially be turned into one of the most positive experiences.

Sometimes tasks need to be broken into steps in order to make them more manageable for people. Someone may not be able to put all the steps into the correct sequence for example in clearing a table. However there are many different smaller tasks involved:

- Picking up cutlery.

- Picking up plates.

- Filling up a washing bowl.

- Putting washing liquid into a bowl.

- Washing items in a bowl.

- Rinsing items.

- Drying up.

- Sorting cutlery into knives, forks and spoons.

- Putting cutlery in cutlery tray.

- Stacking plates together.

- Picking up napkins off the table.

- Putting napkins in the bin.

- Wiping table mats.

- Folding table cloths.

A skilled care worker will know which of these steps might be possible for a person to do, taking into consideration where they are in their experience of their dementia as well as their mobility and other abilities.

There are many simple ways of helping people still feel loved and at HOME inside themselves

The Essence of Friendship

'A friend is someone who knows the song in your heart and can sing it back to you when you have forgotten the words.'

Donna Roberts

Enjoying time with friends is about being with people with whom we have mutual experiences and interests and with whom we feel comfortable. Making new friendships and maintaining old friendships throughout our lives aren't without difficulties. Different life experiences, geographical distance and sometimes illness and death can lead to many losses of friends. However, the true essence of friendship is when we know we are not alone in the world. Whether we see a friend daily or only occasionally we immediately pick up again on the sense of friendship and know we have someone who we can laugh or cry with.

Supporting people to maintain old friendships and make new ones really matters

With increasing frailty and sometimes sensory loss in addition to a dementia, it might seem that it won't be as easy to enjoy friendships. This does not have to be the case!

However, sometimes it helps to think about ways of actively nurturing relationships:

- Putting more sofas in lounges – encourages people to sit together, hold hands and feel close.

- Creating small groupings of chairs so that people can see each other easily and are close enough to make contact with each other.

- Making connections between people who share an interest or a common life experience e.g. two men who support the same football team.

- Using a telephone, Skype or FaceTime for people to 'chat' to family and friends who are at a distance.

- Supporting friends to do something together such as a meal out or walking a dog.

~

Top Tip

People often make their own decisions about who their real friends are - don't be surprised if friendships develop between people of very different backgrounds!

~

Quite often after lunch, people are encouraged to automatically return to soft lounge chairs where they are likely to fall asleep. There is a missed opportunity here as skilled care workers can ensure that after a meal the sociable buzz is maintained by putting things out on tables to generate interest and conversation as this example shows:

A sense of togetherness

Four women shared an enjoyable lunch together and there was much chatter and it felt sociable. The care worker had a plan to keep this sense of togetherness alive – as soon as the table was cleared and before it was even wiped of crumbs the care worker tipped a huge pile of silk flowers onto the table in front of the women. This was received with surprise and enthusiasm as the colourful flowers sat there inviting them to look and touch. The women were quick to start exploring the variety of flowers and excitedly picked them up, admired them and commented to each other about the colours and how beautiful they were.

Then the care worker placed a vase in front of each person and asked if they would like to fill their vase with flowers. This next phase of the activity was met with a new energy and the women took great care to choose the flowers and arrange them. Once again the care worker focused on people's feelings and brought a bag of prizes explaining that they had all done such a great job that they deserved a prize. The bag was offered to each person in turn to choose their prize from a selection of soft animals. Once chosen they admired their animal and showed it to each other. Later sitting in the lounge, they were offered a glass of sherry, port or brandy which they carefully chose for themselves. They relaxed with their drink, their soft animal and sang along to some familiar gentle music together.

Some FRIENDSHIPS develop naturally and some need to be supported to happen and to flourish

The Essence of Conversation

'It's more fun to talk with someone who doesn't use long, difficult words but rather short easy words, like "What about lunch?"'.

Winnie the Pooh, AA Milne

A good chat is one of the most enjoyable activities in life. Someone who takes an interest in what we have to say helps us feel better about ourselves. Listening to others talking can be stimulating too. Stereotypically, British people are particularly keen on talking about the weather but there are many other possibilities! Conversations can involve serious issues, funny stories, topics for debate or just a chance to express how we feel.

Supporting people to find varieties of things to chat about throughout the day matters

Nurses or care workers who are skilled at chatting can open up a much wider range of connections and topics. Many people often have the skill of making conversation naturally. They are the sort of people who can strike up a chat at a bus stop or can encourage a person to share their life story in the hairdresser! However developing the ease of conversation is possible with practice.

Some of the helpful things to think about when starting conversations with people living with a dementia are:

Avoid too many questions especially those that require factual answers e.g. asking someone how many children they have might be very stressful and even upsetting for a person who is unable to recall the answer. Instead make a positive statement such as 'Those children in the photograph look lovely!'

Start talking about a topic yourself to warm the person up before involving them; 'My favourite teacher at school was Mrs Jones. I remember she was tall with very long blonde hair and she was always laughing.' See what response comes.

Opinion based questions are easier than fact based questions as there is no right or wrong answer – 'Do you prefer cats or dogs?' 'I really admire the Queen, do you like her too?'

Use props to stimulate conversation e.g. if you bring out a skipping rope and ask someone to hold the other end of it whilst you turn it round together, this will almost certainly remind people of skipping in the playground and skipping rhymes; 'Salt, pepper, vinegar, mustard..', 'January, February..'

Choose topics that you know might connect to an individual's background and perhaps invite their expertise in a particular area.

Making a shopping list

Gloria is a woman originally from Trinidad who has been a housewife and mother to a large family. She has been sitting looking slightly bored and lost at the kitchen table after lunch. Sarah brings a pad of paper and pen to the table and says that she has to do the shopping list. She asks for Gloria to help but Gloria initially says she is not interested. Sarah starts to write down some items on the list talking out loud; 'Now I wonder about what meat... and cleaning materials..?' Gradually Gloria's face starts to light up and she says 'Don't forget the carnation milk!' She then proceeds to add a lot of items to Sarah's list. Sarah thanks her and Gloria looks really chuffed that she has been able to help.

Chat cards

Create some good conversational starter cards which can be laminated and cut up to put out on tables to give ideas for topics. There will be some trial and error about how these will work with individuals and it is essential that they aren't used in a way that puts people on the spot. With some of the examples below, you might feel that you need to have some knowledge of the person first and a relationship with them before raising a personal topic.

Some examples of conversation starters might be:

- What would you do if you had a million pounds?

- Who was your first love?

- What advice would you give to parents raising children now?

- If you could wave a magic wand and change one thing about this place, what would you want to change?

- What is one thing you would want to thank your parents for?

- If you were Prime Minister, what laws might you make?

- I went shoe shopping yesterday. I love buying shoes! (Show the shoes – wait for a response).

- Your daughter tells me that you are a great gardener and have green fingers. I wish you could give me some advice on my garden! (Wait for a response).

- Do you have a favourite sport? (prompts could include cricket, rugby, boxing, tennis etc. or use pictures).

- My favourite football team is… I wonder if you have a favourite team?

- What would be your idea of a perfect day out?

- I was a Girl Guide. Were you a Boy Scout/Brownie or a Girl Guide?

Sometimes people need practice and support to start up different CONVERSATIONS

The Essence of Play

'A little nonsense now and then is cherished by the wisest men.'

Roald Dahl, Charlie and the Great Glass Elevator

Play is often something which we associate with children. Yet playfulness is a quality that we also enjoy as adults. It is something that connects us with feeling alive and free. It brings humour and energy to a variety of situations. When times are tough, being able to still play can provide a welcome release. Some of us find it hard to allow ourselves to be playful as we feel self-conscious and we think it might make us look silly.

Encouraging an atmosphere in which people can feel able to play matters

When thinking about people living with a dementia, the subject of playfulness has been explored by a range of writers. (Perrin 1997, Perrin and May 2000, Knocker 2002, Killick 2013) It is now more widely accepted that, like all of us, people living with a dementia are likely to benefit from interactions which are playful, especially when they help encourage affection and a sense of fun between people. However, some people in the earlier experiences of a dementia particularly might feel patronised if they think something is 'childish.' After the earlier experiences of a dementia, where people are more in a different reality, the use of dolls and soft toys can create a comfort and a sense of purpose. However families might also find it hard to understand if their relative is holding a doll, a spinning top or other toy. It is therefore very important to take time to explain why some of the things that are appealing to children can also be enjoyed by adults. The feelings evoked by these connections are deep and important.

There are people who naturally have an ability to be playful whether it is dressing up in a funny costume, pulling a silly face or dancing spontaneously in a room. This essence is a very special quality to encourage in a team, and sometimes leaders themselves need to model the approach so that everyone is given permission to discover their playful side.

~

Top Tip

Cultivate the playful members of your team to whom it comes naturally but ensure you also value the 'quieter' Butterflies who offer other qualities.

~

Simple ways to encourage more playfulness:

- Placing hat-stands and dressing up clothes within the entrances of lounges to encourage people to 'make an entrance' in the room.

- Encouraging housekeepers to use colourful feather dusters or puppets to create playful moments whilst they are doing the cleaning.

- Organising days to encourage the team to be playful e.g. 'Wacky Wednesdays' or themed dressing-up days.

- Creating children's play areas in care homes which will encourage younger visitors but also give possibilities for everyone to join in!

- Placing props around the home that encourage playfulness such as bubbles to blow, large beach balls and feather boas.

Kicking leaves

'I went with Mrs Hamble to a small local park where leaves were falling from the trees… Mrs Hamble was still fast asleep. I suddenly had a childish impulse (a great asset in dementia care!) to run through the leaves. So I ran kicking them in the air, lifting my arms up high to catch a falling one, enjoying the crunchy sound of contact with those at my feet and the air and sunshine on my face. Gradually Mrs Hamble's face started to lift from her slumber as she noticed my movement and energy. She started to smile and then called out with great animation, 'Run, RUN!' In that moment, her 96-year-old face became transformed – awake, alert, alive! It was as if she had been transported in time and was six years old again in her mind and in her heart running in the leaves alongside me. Through watching another person in that moment, she was able to leave behind her weak body and tired mind to find a place that was light and fun and free again.' (Knocker 2010).

Adults sometimes need to be given permission to PLAY, but once this is achieved, many magic loving moments will follow!

10 The Essence of Groups

'Having embraced the concept of matching, I am amazed at how this approach works. People living, working and visiting here have all their individual strengths, abilities and interests recognised. By supporting their attributes we have enhanced each person's wellbeing and sense of self-worth – truly inspirational and heart-warming.'

Anita Astle, Wren Hall Nursing Home

As human beings we don't often choose to spend time in very large groups unless we are a member of a team or a community group. When we meet with people in small social groups it is generally because they are people with similar interests or they share some connection such as work or children at the same school. Sometimes we do choose to meet in groups in order to learn something new, or we might turn to a group for support and nurturing.

Bringing people together at similar points in their experience of a dementia matters

When thinking about groups of people living with a dementia there will of course be friendships which develop and people who choose to spend time with each other. In an ideal world this would be the main criteria for grouping people in living areas in care homes. However when a person is living with a dementia, there are complex additional factors which need to be considered when bringing people together in group living.

The ideal care home setting is where a person would receive one-to-one care and support. This in dementia care is very rarely going to happen. The reality of living in a care home is that there is a need to balance individualised care and group-living with staff resources. All group-living throughout life requires elements of compromise. Living in a care home will be no different.

The 'matching' approach

This approach advocates that people living with a dementia can be better supported to live life well if they are grouped with people at a similar point in their experience of dementia.

Our promotion of the 'Matching' approach is inspired by the work of Naomi Feil, the developer of Validation Therapy (Feil and De Clerk-Rubin 2012) and others have acknowledged the value of identifying 'stages' in relation to specialist approaches to occupation and activity (Pool 2012).

Like any journey people living with a dementia may often appear to be in-between different points of a dementia and the journey for each person will progress at a different pace.

When people at different points in their journey are all muddled up, there are many potential difficulties:

- People in the earlier points of a dementia may be critical or upset by someone in the later experiences; 'Why is that man cuddling a doll?' 'What is she doing eating her food with her fingers?'
- People who are expressing themselves through repetitive words or actions may need particular support to move from being 'stuck' in these emotions – others may find these repetitive behaviours hard to live with.
- People in the later experiences are less likely to receive focused one-to-one time or may find what can appear as the over-busy activity of people in a different reality quite unsettling.
- Care workers have to try and switch between very different styles of relating to people which is demanding and tiring.

'Muddling people up together at different points of experience of a dementia, with associated different 'stages' of losses, is most likely to cause increased stress and anxiety. Grouping people together at similar points of experience of a dementia gives people the best chance to achieve the most from their remaining strengths. This grouping together also gives staff the best chance to focus their skills at people's different points of dementia.'

(Sheard 2011)

Working with matched groups of people at a similar point of dementia gives the chance for team members to recognise where their personality and skills brings out the best in both those living and those working there.

This is not about labelling people, nor about restricting people's free movement, nor about preventing friendships. However, Dementia Care Matters' extensive experience has shown that some of the very best

dementia care is provided where an environment and approach are focused on people living at a similar point in their dementia. The aim is to bring out the best in people by providing a home that 'makes sense' to them in relation to where they are in their dementia.

Some care homes are developing the 'Household' model (Sheard 2013) which creates independent small 'houses' within larger care homes that each have a separate front door and very distinct identity. A household for people in the earlier experiences, for example, will be much more like a 'normal' house in terms of the provision of a kitchen which is regularly used for domestic activities and a living room with everyday domestic objects magazines, books and ornaments to stimulate conversation.

In a household for people in repetitive experiences, there will be lots of engaging sensory items to connect with where skilled care workers respond to the feelings which might be being expressed by people through repeated words and actions.

A household for people in later experiences will have a quieter feel with a focus on using all the senses to engage people – this might include decorations on ceilings where people who are lying down for long periods may well be looking upwards. Access to an outside garden area might also be especially important for people at this point in their journey.

The ideas for occupation and activity that are detailed in Appendix 1 will need to be adapted according to what point of dementia the person is experiencing.

Just as in life people are drawn together with a commonality so too in dementia care when people can't make that self-selection, specialist dementia care workers need to help people to spend their day in a household that brings out the best in both people living and working there.

When thinking about people spending time together in GROUPS, matching people at similar points in their experience of a dementia can ensure an environment and opportunities for occupation that make sense to people

11

The Essence of Structure

'I know a lot of us feel that structured group activities are less and less relevant in care homes these days, but some people really like the fact that they know the exercise group is always on Wednesdays and the choir meets on Sundays.'

Jasmine, Activity Co-ordinator in a care home

If we think about the way we organise our lives, there are some things which are regular planned activities such as going to a hairdresser or taking part in a weekly sports event, and some which we decide on the day or even in the moment. Some structure in our lives provides a sense of security. Meeting up with friendly faces and going through the familiar rituals in a gathering that we are regularly a part of feels reassuring.

Creating opportunities for some planned and structured groups and events during the week matters

In many of Dementia Care Matters' Butterfly Service homes, there is more of a focus on creating a relaxed feel to the day. This is so that many of the things that happen are spontaneous rather than planned. However there are some individuals, particularly those who are earlier on in their experience of a dementia, who may enjoy a more structured social activity. Some thought needs to be given, as with any social gathering, as to who might benefit. Focusing on what the 'mix' of people might be in terms of where they are in their dementia as well as personalities and interests is important. This will need some planning in advance. Ideally there should be two members of the team involved in any group, so that one can 'hold' the whole group whilst the other can 'flit' and respond to individual needs. Both people can also benefit from supporting each other.

There are many excellent publications which can assist in ideas for group activity possibilities. (Bowden and Lewthwaite 2009, NAPA 2010, Zoutewelle-Morris 2011)

Think about including the following core ingredients to include in your group:

- Something **mentally stimulating** – using the mind and memory.
- Something **physical** – getting the body moving and the voice working.
- Something **sensory** – using items to look at, touch, smell, taste or listen to.
- Something **fun** – finding ways of encouraging people to laugh and enjoy themselves.

You will need to find ways to include people who have sensory or other physical difficulties, in terms of where people will sit and who will support them.

The group should include:

- Introductions and a 'starter' activity to warm people up to the topic being introduced.
- Some main activities to include the physical, mental, sensory and fun aspects from above.
- A closing circle to indicate the end of the group – for example with a song or a thought for the day.

Example – Topic of Transport and Travel

Starter activity – Welcome each person in the group by name. Pass round a model train, bus, boat, aeroplane and bicycle and talk about the journeys people have been on and what would be their favourite way of travelling? Ensure people living and working together share their own experiences of travelling and favourite journeys.

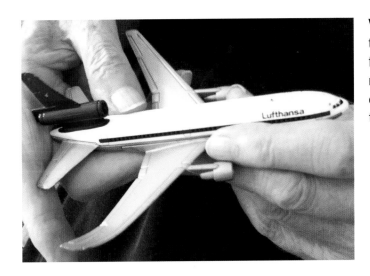

Word game – On a board, put up the word 'FLY AN AEROPLANE' and find how many other words you can make out of these letters. Or do an anagram of AEROPLANE and ask the group to work out the word.

Quiz – Transport related questions, or a 'sounds' quiz of noises made by different transport.

Pictures of different kinds of cars, aeroplanes and trains (over the last 70 years) – comment on makes and design – how have they changed over time? Share a poem about travel.

Magic carpet – hold a large colourful sheet in a circle and talk about desired locations to travel to. Bounce a soft ball or balloon.

Closing circle – songs linked to travel: 'Row, row, row your boat…', 'Daisy, Daisy….' 'Show me the way to go home.'

This structure is only a guide and a skilled group facilitator will know when to 'go with the flow' – for example a group about transport may develop into a group about favourite pets!

Opportunities for being occupied include some STRUCTURED planned events as well as spontaneous activities throughout the day

12

The Essence of Surroundings

'I feel it in my fingers, I feel it in my toes, Love is all around me, And so the feeling grows.'

Wet, Wet, Wet

When we enter any building or room for the first time, we often get a strong sense of whether it is a place where we feel that there is love or not. The objects in a room might spark interest in us or not, for example if there are books on the shelves or patterned cushions on the sofa. If there are dirty cups in the sink, we might be prompted to go and do the washing up. If there is a comfortable chair by the window with a view of the garden, we might be drawn to sit down and relax. The 'Look' of somewhere usually really matters to us and influences our feelings and behaviours.

Creating an environment that is colourful, engaging and welcoming matters

A real butterfly cannot flourish or even survive in a concrete car park. Care home butterflies will struggle to flourish in tidy, sterile lounges with magnolia walls, hotel style pictures and empty tables.

In order to stimulate interest in a room, it helps to fill up the environment at different parts of the day with various items to engage people. This can be seen as a bit like theatre staging in that it requires some thought rather than just randomly putting lots of stuff everywhere. The idea is to create invitations to people to pick things up, sort things or finish a particular activity.

These are some of the ideas which have worked well:

- Writing the words of songs in decorative paint down a hallway to inspire people to sing.

- Creating an indoor garden theme for lounges for people in later experiences including murals of trees and skies, silk flowers, bird song music etc.

- Making interesting places to visit for example a shoe shop complete with boxes of shoes, a bar area or an old telephone box.

- Designing themed corners for example a baby's nursery with a large pram, a seaside themed area or a theatre and dressing-up clothes box to encourage playfulness.

- Copying home-like features like a domestic laundry-style area with washing line, ironing board etc.

- Hanging up lots of hand-bags, scarves and items that are easy to pick up and put on.

- Leaving books and magazines open on tables so they are more likely to be read.

For all of the above ideas, it will be important to check current fire regulations and follow other health and safety guidance in relation to where items are placed with proper consideration for any possible risks involved.

Some people visiting Butterfly Service homes feel that rooms look too 'busy' and cluttered or that the colours are too bright. However, all the evidence of our detailed observations over the years shows that the 'stuff' in the surroundings can enable people to connect even when there are no workers present.

'Do you ever look at a place and think; I could really be busy in here… they've filled the place up; this place looks like a place full of memories, this place looks full of stuff to do with people's past jobs, this place has got comfort things that you could touch and feel…?' ('Look' in Mattering DVD, 2013).

David Sheard

Ideally a room or area will be filled with 'stuff' that links in some way to people living there in relation to people's backgrounds and interests or possibly links to something which is happening in the wider world, for example Wimbledon Tennis or St David's Day.

What about if things go missing constantly? This should be seen as a positive as it usually means people in the home are enjoying picking things up and putting items in their handbags or taking things into their own bedrooms.

In order to fill up the environment, it can be helpful to enlist the help of families, workers and visitors. A sample poster is included in Appendix 2, which gives some ideas for the kinds of things the home might need.

Creating SURROUNDINGS which are colourful and stimulating can provide many opportunities for connecting

13 The Essence of Life Themes

'Having a range of themed boxes created by the whole team has really generated some buzz in the place. We can now easily bring boxes out and put things out on tables and then the talking starts!'

Christina, Activity Co-ordinator

Whilst everyone's life brings many different experiences, there are many recurring themes, which people will relate to. The topics might relate to life events like 'Weddings' or 'Babies' or to particular interests like 'Sport' or 'Gardening'. For other people, local, national or world events or places of significance might prompt the most interest. Life themes are the things that bring us together in terms of shared human experiences and the things that connect us with memories of particular people, places and events in our lives.

Connecting with people linked to key life themes and using varieties of props matters

One way of ensuring that the environment gets filled with different things at different times of the day and on different days is to create boxes. These boxes need to be linked to themes and be visible on open shelves in the lounge so that they can be brought out at regular intervals.

The type of box you use can vary – a Perspex box so you can easily see the contents can be good or a box shaped to your theme for example a decorative hat box for the 'Weddings' theme. If you are doing a memory box for an individual, it might be helpful to have it decorated in images related to that person's life story, and for it to be small enough to be on a table beside them.

Housekeepers need to be on board with the purpose of the boxes and to be encouraged not to 'tidy things away' all the time!

Designated members of the team need to be given the role of maintaining the boxes which will mean ensuring that items are returned to the correct box at end of the shift, items are checked and cleaned regularly and that new 'stuff' is constantly found to replenish boxes.

~

The following are possible themes:

- Weddings
- Holidays
- Maps – local, national, world
- Transport – trains, planes, bicycles, buses etc.
- Pets and animals
- Household – cleaning materials and equipment, popular food packets etc.
- Places of interest – Wales, Ireland, Birmingham etc.
- Fashion
- Film stars
- Food and drink
- Babies and children
- Shopping
- School days
- Sports
- Days out
- Beauty and Pampering
- Royal Family

You might create boxes linked to the particular group interests of individuals living in the home or possibly a box for a specific person.

In each box try and include:

- Things to touch and feel, taste, listen to, smell and look at.
- Song sheets connected to the theme.
- Pictures.
- Chat cards with possible conversation starters.
- Poems or stories.
- Quiz questions.

Boxes will need to be adapted for different lounge areas e.g. quiz questions will not be relevant for people in the later experiences and there will need to be more tactile objects for people in repetitive sensory experiences to fiddle with.

Avoiding empty laps

It is not enough to just place items in the environment and hope that people will connect with them. For some individuals who are very active this can work well, but for many people in the repetitive sensory or later experiences of a dementia, it is dependent on care workers to bring items to the person. The skill of a dementia specialist worker is to get a sense of what might work well for particular individuals and to give these to people at particular points of the day to reduce long periods of boredom and sleepiness.

- A man living with a dementia who used to be an electrician is given some fibre optic lights to hold – he spends nearly an hour engrossed in twisting, sorting and pulling them with great attention and focus.

- A bowl of crispy rice cereal with strawberry jam and a wooden spoon is placed on the lap of a woman who is looking quite withdrawn– she grips the bowl, gradually starts to stir and then puts her finger in the mix to taste it – she is happily occupied for half an hour.

- A doll is given to a man living with a dementia – he holds her very gently and then raises her up and down on his lap singing to her with great love and joy in his eyes.

When developing resources to positively occupy people, think about key LIFE THEMES and what might be particularly relevant to individuals

14 The Essence of the Senses

*'When something is new to us, we treat it as an experience.
We feel that our senses are awake and clear. We are alive.'*

Jasper Johns

All of us relate to the world through our senses. For some of us a smell or a sound might help us remember a special person or a particular event in our lives. Many of us will describe experiences in relation to what we saw, heard or tasted for example. All of these sensory experiences connect us strongly with our feelings and memories.

Ensuring that we make the most of all the five main senses when connecting to people matters

When thinking about bringing positive experiences to people living with a dementia, the focus is on ensuring every area has things which appeal to: **SOUND, TOUCH, TASTE, SMELL** and **SIGHT**.

If this sensory approach is used in relation to daily living activities it can become a much more positive experience.

Spicing up an everyday task: for example serving tea or coffee

Step one: Get rid of the tea trolley and set tea times!

SIGHT – use interesting pretty crockery – pour tea in front of people, put out pictures or objects to prompt conversations.

SOUND – choose music to create a party mood, the clutter of plates and the chat as you serve – be creative e.g. the noise of a kettle whistling can be recorded and played!

TOUCH – put out things to pick up – milk jugs, sugar bowls, cakes and biscuits, prepare scones or sandwiches, fold serviettes, and stack plates after tea.

TASTE – think about including different taste experiences – different teas, strawberries and cream.

SMELL – coffee percolators creating coffee smells, baking cakes before tea.

~

Top Tip

For someone in the later experiences of a dementia, things need to be close at hand to encourage care workers to interact and connect with a person: a small table beside each individual with items related to their life history and interests for example a football scarf for a football fan or a typewriter for a secretary.

~

ENGAGE THE MIND OR MEMORY – ask people whether they like milk in first or after in their tea or cream or jam first on a scone – have a themed tea party e.g. a 'Pink' theme or a 'Rock and Roll' theme and choose music, food and decorations related to the theme.

In many Butterfly Service homes, workers wear 'Activity' belts with large pockets so that they can have items to bring out and help create connections with people. Fill the pockets with objects that tap into each of the five senses such as personal photographs, massage cream, bells, bubbles, string, lace, etc.

Connecting with the senses will be especially important for people in the later experiences of a dementia. As an individual's dementia progresses, it has been described as becoming more like being in a 'bubble' where the world comes in closer. People at this point in their lives will only experience a 'world' in very close proximity to their line of vision. If a person also has sight difficulties, then the noises, smells and textures around them might be more significant. Therefore providing 'closeness' and filling up a person's world very close to them in a 'wrap around' or cocooning sense becomes key.

Take some time in the day to go and sit closely alongside a person in the later experiences of a dementia and assess what they might be experiencing from the position they are sitting or lying in. Where are the person's eyes looking? What sounds might the person be hearing? How comfortable do their neck, arms and legs appear? Is there something in their close world that might cause fear or distress? Is there anything you can change to bring more comfort or interest for that person?

Some examples are given in Appendix 3 on maximising the use of the senses in a dementia care home.

Making use of all of the SENSES offers many different opportunities to experience variety and pleasure in the day

15

The Essence of Music

'If music be the food of love, play on…'

Twelfth Night, William Shakespeare

Music for many links us to people, places and events in our lives. Our mood can change in a moment listening to music as there is a strong connection between music and our emotions. We use music to relax, to celebrate, to remember, to dance and to share our love with others in a variety of ways. Music we don't like or which has an unhappy association can also have a powerful impact on how we feel.

Paying attention to the right variety, 'mood' and individual and group preferences of music matters

The single easiest way to lift the atmosphere in the room is to use music. It is another part of life in a home that deserves time, attention and leadership.

Music obviously needs to be tailored to the taste of the individuals who are living there and as times are moving on, it is vital not to get stuck in a 'time warp' of the 1940s or 1950s!

A useful starting point is to ensure that you have a good range including the following types of music:

- Strauss waltzes.
- Other dance collections – Salsa, Tango, Scottish dance, Irish Jigs, Steel band, Bollywood etc.
- Rock and Roll – Bill Hayley and the Comets etc.
- Sixties and Seventies Pop Music, The Beatles, Gerry and The Pacemakers, Abba, Led Zeppelin!?
- Country music.
- Classical collections – opera, orchestral.
- The musicals – 'My Fair Lady', 'The Sound of Music', 'Oklahoma'.
- Pub song classics – 'The Lambeth Walk', 'Show Me The Way To Go home'.

- Music to inspire movement and fun – Hokey Cokey, Zorba the Greek, the Can Can.

- Peaceful meditative music for quieter times.

- Sounds of nature.

- Some of the classic artists over time; Elvis Presley, Michael Bublé, Tom Jones, Queen!

- Karaoke collections – with words on screen.

Creating playlists for individuals linked to their life stories and interests

The Radio 4 programme 'Desert Island discs' invites celebrities to choose a selection of tracks which they talk about in relation to their own life stories. Skilled care workers are realising that the right choice of music can have a powerful impact on a person's wellbeing. Modern technology makes it relatively easy to compile playlists for individuals.

The challenge in many cases is to identify the music that might be of significance to that individual especially when the person doesn't have close relatives involved. If a manager or senior worker goes to an individual's house prior to them living in a care home, there is an opportunity to ask about or have a look at the music that the person has in their own homes. There may also be favourite films or books which can be identified and brought with the person to the care home.

Use of MUSIC deserves as much expertise as the administration of medicine as it is one of the best 'medicines' of all!

16 The Essence of Watching

'I turned George's wheelchair to face the window and we watched the sun going down over the houses in the distance together. We sat there in silence for only about five minutes but it felt very special. He turned to me and smiled and then squeezed my hand.'

Jeff, maintenance person in a care home

How much time do we take to stop and watch the world around us? As we walk to the shops, sit on a train or open the curtains in the morning, it is easy to miss things. This might be something in the natural environment like a squirrel on a tree or another person having an animated discussion with a friend. If we took time to stop and notice, there are many different 'dramas' unfolding right on our doorstep.

Creating lots of opportunities for people to enjoy watching things happening in daily life matters

There are so many missed opportunities in care homes for people to benefit from watching things going on. Many of us can take pleasure in observing the world around us as it helps us feel alive and connected to other people.

This might be as simple as ensuring that tea is served at a table in front of individuals with milk jug and sugar pot there, so that a person is involved in the process, even if they are too physically frail to pour the tea and milk themselves.

Some of the most natural 'butterflies' in care homes can be team members from supporting roles in maintenance, domestic, kitchen or administration. However, they do not always know that they too can be butterflies and so may need some encouragement to 'come out of their chrysalis.' (NAPA 2010)

Invite workers to think about all the jobs they do in the day which might be opportunities for people to watch and/ or get involved.

~

The following might be great things for individuals to watch:

- A maintenance person doing some decorating, changing a light bulb or putting up a picture.

- A laundry worker sorting through clothes, sheets or towels.

- An administrator on the telephone or doing some paperwork.

- A gardener mowing the lawn or doing some planting, pruning or watering.

- A child playing.

- The comings and goings in the reception area or the car park.

- A care worker doing some knitting.

- Birds on the bird table.

- The sun setting.

- Rain on the window panes.

Many of these 'watching' activities could also become opportunities to involve someone in participating for example helping folding the sheets, holding the light bulb for the maintenance person or the wool for the person knitting.

Get rid of the 'net curtains' on life – open our eyes and enjoy WATCHING the things that are happening all around us!

17 The Essence of Stillness

*'… But will you permit me to say
that you have the stillness of silence,
that listens and lasts.'*

(From 'You Are Words' Dementia Poems, Edited by John Killick)

> Stillness is both a quality and an experience and in both cases can be rare to find in busy lives for many of us. It can often be found in moments in contact with nature such as listening to the song of a blackbird at dusk on a quiet summer evening. In order to achieve stillness in connection with others, it is as important that our mind is not cluttered by too many thoughts so that we can be fully present, mindful and attentive for the other person.

Supporting people to discover ways to give full attention and stillness to those who others may forget, matters

The 'Butterfly' which is able to stop on the quietest flower and take a bit more time to 'just be' has a particularly special role to play.

There will be times when a person living with a dementia will not respond to any of the objects that you offer or even appear to notice that you are there. When none of the ideas in this book seem to work you may feel very helpless and lost for what to do. The person may appear very sleepy or disconnected with all that is going on around them. At times like this it is very easy to give up and find another person in the room who is more likely to respond.

Instead Stop and Stay:

- Consider setting aside a minimum of ten minutes to really focus on that individual and let your colleagues know that you are doing this so you won't get pulled away to 'do' other things.

- Sit in a position where you can closely observe the person and make eye contact.

~

Top Tip

Don't be discouraged if sometimes all your best efforts don't seem to result in very visible responses from a person, or even lead to a 'negative' reaction. Try again at another time or on another day, or explore a different approach. Share with your colleagues and learn from each other.

~

- Pay attention to the person's breathing – try matching with your own breaths.

- Look in the same direction the person is looking in – pay close attention to what they might be seeing – comment on what you see.

- Offer your hand – notice the way in which their hand responds to yours – does the person's hand tighten, withdraw or just remain still?

- Gentle stroking movements on the cheek, hand or arm can sometimes connect with a person and are reminiscent of the loving strokes of a mother with a child.

- Stay in silence for a while – this might enable the person to initiate some kind of connection even if it is to give eye contact, make a sound or move their hand or foot.

- Use short simple sentences if you talk and a warm, calm, friendly tone.

- Try reading aloud from something you think might be of interest to that person if you know their background – a book about aeroplanes, a gardening magazine or a poem – watch to see the person's facial expressions as you do this – but don't expect an immediate response of any kind.

- Consider going outside as the air or sun on a person's face and the sights and sounds of a garden can sometimes awaken a connection.

Sometimes loving STILLNESS is the most precious gift you can offer a person living with a dementia

18 The Essence of Time

'We don't have enough time.'

All of our lives are controlled to some extent by times – work times, school times, bedtimes, appointments and meetings. There is often a sense that we are rushed or that we haven't the time to do all the things we want to do in a day. However, when we feel that we have time to just 'be' and not to have to worry or to rush, it makes a huge difference to our wellbeing.

Seeing Time as a 'gift' rather than as a 'problem' matters

Lack of time is usually the most common reason given in care homes for not finding time to be with people. Staffing levels, lots of jobs that have to be done and increasing dependency levels of people living in homes are all seen as barriers to doing more 'activities'.

There are key ways of addressing these barriers:

- Recognising and increasing all the small things that you can do to help create moments throughout the day.

- Transforming the 'task' into an experience – seeing every routine in the day as an opportunity to connect with people and to find pleasure.

- Ensuring that every time someone goes into a room or through a room, they make connections with people.

This is where the 'flitting' element of the butterfly becomes very important. There may be lovely moments in lounges where a few individuals are enjoying special one-to-one time with care workers, but people in the rest of the room are asleep or looking bored. The art of being a butterfly is to make sure that you find ways to reach out and connect with as many people as you can – these might only be brief moments in terms of time, but they ensure that no 'flower' in the garden is left neglected. The use of the stuff in the environment can really help create Butterfly moments for example blowing bubbles into the room, showing a group of people a family photograph or folding a few towels. These activities take moments but can transform the mood in a whole room.

The American 'Best Friends' approach to activities with people living with a dementia (Bell 2004) gives some great ideas for activities that take less than 30 seconds. Dementia Care Matters has produced its own equivalent lists of simple activities that take under a minute which are included here. (See Appendix 4)

There are a lot of simple things which can be done to change the moment which take very little TIME!

19 The Essence of the Day

'It takes every one of us to make this work – free up your staff from fixed ideas and routines – lead your team to believe this and go with the flow.'

Eve Carder

We can all think of 'good days' and 'bad days' in our life. There are days when we wish we hadn't got out of bed and those when we would love to revisit the feelings and experiences we had which made the day special. The essence of a good day will be different for everyone but for many of us, they will be days where we have felt free to do what we want and when we want. Good days will often involve being with people we love and doing the things which bring us pleasure or a sense of achievement. A 'good day' usually runs smoothly but might still have some element of fun and surprise.

Inspirational leadership to create a day which flows and brings out the best in everyone matters

In care homes it can be difficult to remain focused on making a difference to people's experience of a day. There is always the pressure of tasks to be done, paperwork to be completed and a variety of different expectations of how we 'should' be spending our time. An over emphasis on particular job roles can prevent a fluidity and flexibility in the day. If the team gets too rigid about whose job it is to do particular 'tasks', they may miss lots of opportunities to connect as the day unfolds. Encouraging people to 'go with the flow' is one of the biggest challenges. Most people find it clearer to follow familiar ways of doing things and will find a change in approach quite stressful.

The interesting element of this essence is that although the aim is to create a very relaxed and informal feel to the day, it still requires very clear leadership, organisation and planning to make this happen! Using handovers to reflect on some of the 'wow' moments and to ensure a team feels motivated and nurtured for the shift ahead is a really important part of this process. If there is a designated Activity Co-ordinator in the home, it is especially important that the focus is on enabling the whole team to bring activity into all elements of the day, not 'doing' all the 'activities' themselves.

One of the ways to plan, organise and lead the day is to focus on the different points in the day:

Morning – when people are being supported to get up, there are many opportunities for one to one connections such as choosing clothes, bed-making and sorting laundry. These can be done with the person rather than for the person. At breakfast time place toast racks on the table, butter in dishes and jams and marmalades displayed in pots to enable people to help themselves. Complete this experience by joining the person and sharing breakfast with them.

Mid-morning – organise a walk to the local shop to collect a paper and washing up the breakfast things. Do some polishing and general household chores and maintenance workers can involve people connected to past work life or hobbies. Go for a trip to the 'Cafe table' created by the night team for mid-morning tea and cakes. Remember to use a teapot, milk in a jug and sugar in a bowl, enable people to serve themselves and watch them flourish as they serve you and the person next to them.

Before Lunch – provide nibbles to stimulate taste buds. Create conversations about the setting up of tables and enable people to set tables in their way without correcting them. Be sure to praise and thank people for helping. Placing a box on each table full of conversation starters will support people to sit at a table for longer, leading to meals being finished and second helpings enjoyed; weight-gain will be the evidence for this.

Just After Lunch – enable people to experience the positive feelings of being needed and feeling useful by encouraging them to clear tables and wash up (the dishes will go through the dishwasher afterwards, food hygiene requirements will not be compromised). Whilst people are around the table use the opportunity for a baking session that can be served later for afternoon tea. Try some board games, another cup of tea and a chat; vacuuming or brushing the floor are all ways to occupy people at this time.

Post Lunch – people can be very tired after such a busy morning so be ready to increase the use of comfort items. Cocoon someone in a blanket who has dropped off to sleep so that they can experience comfort and closeness even if they wake up with no one sat next to them. There is no need for empty laps at this time. Someone can be asleep but when they wake up will notice and pick up the book or paper that has been placed in front of them or cuddle the baby or cushion that has been placed in their arms.

Before Tea Time – time to maybe light the fire and get ready for tea with food preparation by involving people in making sandwiches and desserts. People living with a dementia can be as involved as staff. (To feel confident about food hygiene standards ensure preparation surfaces are thoroughly cleaned, thorough hand washing and a domestic style apron is worn rather than plastic). Someone who wants to be involved will wash their hands too and the aprons being worn are a fantastic talking point. Encouraging someone to serve sandwiches to others will create a sense of satisfaction. If a tray of sandwiches goes 'wrong' simply throw it away.

Evening and Night Time – some people will want to settle down whilst others will come to life. The occupation and involvement of people needs to be paced according to each individual. Creating a quiet sensory based lounge in the evening with relaxing music, low lighting and the use of oils (risk assessments permitting) to stimulate different senses will suit some people. An alternative can be another lounge for people to be preparing for their 'next day at work' or settling the babies for the night. Think about involving people in other night time jobs like closing the curtains in lounges and bedrooms.

The opportunities for occupation at different times of the day are endless, think outside of the box and make it reality!

> # It takes a whole team and whole DAY approach to make connecting and occupying a way of life in a home

20 The Essence of the 'S' Factor

'Smile, it's the key that fits the lock of everybody's heart.'

Anthony J. D'Angelo

We all know people who can light up a room with their presence. There is an energy and warmth about them which makes us want to smile. There are people with the 'S' factor in all walks of life – you can see it in people's eyes and in the way that they relate to others. Some people with the 'S' factor will have a particularly playful personality or colourful or unusual appearance. The 'sparkle' they can bring to a room is infectious and mood lifting. However there are also individuals with a calmer quality that have the softer 'S' factor – their gentle loving presence helps us feel we are in safe hands.

Cultivating and celebrating the 'S' factor in your team matters

The following represents some of the key essences of what we all need to be doing more of in life:

SMILE a lot – nothing is as simple and as effective at changing moments!

SLOW down – don't let tasks take over.

SPEAK to people and be with people.

SHARE your own life and moments, memories and meals.

SEE and SENSE when someone needs you to be with them.

SIT AND STAY – spending time with people is the most important job of all.

SPARKLE – don't forget to add a bit of SPARKLE when you can!

Don't make assumptions about people when you first see them – it's what's inside not what's outside which counts!

Fire exit
Keep clear

Conclusion:
The Essence of People

'What is the most important thing in the world? He tangata, he tangata, he tangata. It is people, it is people, it is people'

Old Maori saying

In order to create days which are filled with variety, companionship, love and meaningful connections, there are lots of practical things that we can do. We can decorate the walls and fill the lounges, we can organise groups, make community links and plan events and trips out. However, the most important ingredient of all is the 'magic' that all the people in a home bring moment by moment and day by day. Every person in a care home community is as different and important as the diversity of butterflies in a garden.

Each 'essence' explored in this book is vital in itself but if we combine all these essences together, we start to see the full colour and splendour of the butterfly.

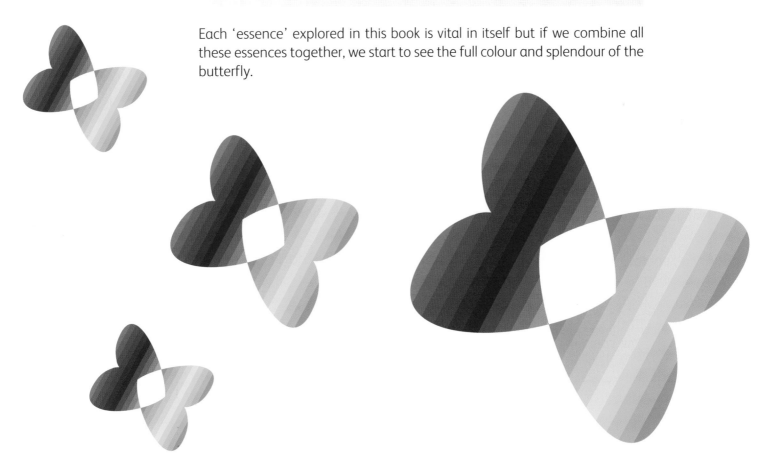

Appendix 1: Ideas linked to people's different needs

Everyday life

- Making a cup of tea/coffee
- Preparing food
- Going to the shop to buy a paper or post a letter
- Listening to the radio
- Talking to someone on the phone
- Stroking or feeding a cat or dog
- Watching children playing
- Helping someone out
- Watching the world go by out the window
- Noticing the change of seasons and the weather
- Lying with feet up on the sofa
- Placing a bet on the horses
- Looking at the sport pages in the newspapers
- Checking the football results and fixtures
- Doing a 'Spot the ball' or football 'Pools' coupon

N.B. Find out what is 'normal life' for each person whilst they were living at home and ask how can we continue this?

Talking and Reminiscing

- Looking at pictures or maps of the local area
- Talking about old household items, old toys, fashion items
- Exploring memory boxes linked to themes e.g. 'Ireland', 'Childhood', 'Transport', 'Holidays', 'Sport'
- Discussing the news
- Talking to a family member on Skype or FaceTime
- Using a tablet (iPad or other) to look up topics of interest

The Arts and Culture

- Painting/Aqua painting
- Pottery/Sculpture
- Taking/looking at photographs
- Creating life story albums
- Going to an art gallery exhibition or a theatre
- Going to a concert or choir recital
- Watching a film
- Going to the library or a museum

Stimulating the mind

- Answering quiz questions
- Doing a crossword puzzle
- Discussing old sayings
- Reading or listening to poetry
- Word games – boys' names beginning with 'B', something you find at a wedding beginning with A, B, C…
- Looking through travel or shopping catalogues and making a wish list
- Writing a letter or a birthday card/ sending an email
- Debating a topic of interest
- Listening to a talking book
- Doing some maths e.g. reciting times tables
- Playing dominos, scrabble or other board game
- Looking at books or the internet linked to individual interests – recipes, cars, cats etc.

Movement/physical	Musical	Spiritual
• Throwing balls or balloons	• Using percussion instruments	• Spending some quiet time in the day
• Armchair exercises	• An individual music player and earphones for individuals who have particular taste in music	• Saying a prayer
• Playing bowls or skittles		• Singing a hymn
• Playing floor basketball		• Saying the Rosary
• Playing games on the 'Wii'	• Inviting people living, working in or visiting the home to perform; play an instrument, sing a song	• Playing some religious music
• Dancing – try ballroom, country, salsa		• Watching a sunrise or a sunset
	• Guessing the name of the song	• Visiting a place of worship
• Holding a parachute or big Lycra or cloth sheet and bouncing a ball or toy on it	• Using a microphone or a Karaoke machine	• Watching a religious programme on the television or listening on the radio
• Holding a large sensory elastic and moving and stretching together	• Inviting in outside musicians – school or church choirs, dancing groups etc. to perform	• Observing key events in the faith calendar for a person of faith
• Playing darts or Pool	• Organising a tea dance	
• Playing mini golf – putting	• Ensuring you know playlists that suit individual tastes	
• Walking 'round the block' or building – feed the birds, post a letter, visit a friend	• Organising CD players or radios in people's own rooms and checking preferred channels or CDs	
• Washing a car		
• Doing some gardening		
• Pushing a pram		
• Walking a dog		
• Going swimming		

Domestic

- Dusting
- Discussing recipes
- Sweeping leaves
- Brushing the floor
- Brass polishing
- Cleaning windows
- Washing up/Drying up
- Ironing
- Laying tables
- Clearing tables
- Making or stripping beds
- Folding – sheets, serviettes etc.
- Chopping or peeling vegetables
- Preparing sandwiches
- Rolling/moulding dough
- Stirring ingredients in a bowl
- Icing or decorating cakes
- Doing some DIY – putting up a picture, sanding a door
- Decorating
- Sorting things – pairing socks, tidying a tool box
- Watering plants, weeding, pruning

Comfort/security

- Cradling and nursing a doll
- Holding/cuddling a soft toy
- Stroking an animal
- Looking at photographs
- Listening to a favourite piece of music
- Saying a prayer
- Holding hands
- Having a hug or a cuddle
- Going for a walk
- Enjoying a hot water bottle or a hot drink at bedtime
- Reading aloud to someone

Fun

- Creating a themed event – e.g. 'Tea party Tuesday', 'Wacky Wednesdays'
- Celebrating particular diary occasions such as a sporting event
- Playing music which encourages playfulness; 'Zorba the Greek', the 'Hokey Cokey'…
- Dancing with a feather boa or a feather duster!?
- Playing a miming game
- Trying out story telling
- Using puppets
- Having a visit from an Ice Cream van in the summer
- Playing 'peek a boo' with a visiting toddler

Sorting and rummaging

- Looking through handbags
- Rummage feely bags/different textures
- Sorting, untangling or winding wool
- Re-arranging or taking things out of drawers
- Looking at and trying on jewellery
- Feeling things in boxes and baskets with different colours and textures
- Trying on hats and shoes and scarves
- Sorting money into piles/currencies
- Pairing socks

Work life

- Doing an activity linked to previous occupation e.g. fetching eggs, folding laundry, doing accounts
- Office work –answering the phone, stuffing envelopes
- Cleaning work (see domestic)
- Screwing and fitting things together
- Asking for help or advice from someone related to their work expertise

Sensory

- Massage (head, hand, body)
- Manicure, facial or foot spa
- Brushing your own or someone else's hair
- Aromatherapy oils
- Wrapping up or unwrapping presents
- Untying knots
- Polishing shoes/brass etc.
- Relaxing with soft music
- Smelling flowers, fruit, perfumes
- Listening to bird song or animal noises
- Playing sounds linked to memories – church bells
- Playing favourite songs or film clips from YouTube
- Holding / squeezing balls with different textures
- Visual images – aquarium, a log fire, sky or seascapes, forests, children playing
- Stacking 'Jenga' or other wood blocks
- Blowing bubbles
- Arranging flowers
- Making cards or collages
- Tasting something different – spicy, salty, sweet or sour, alcoholic

Appendix 2: Poster for finding things to fill the environment

Sensory

- Squidgy items to hold
- Smelling packs – spices
- Busy aprons and waistcoats
- 'busy' tablecloths
- Bubbles
- Balls of wool, ribbons
- Fruit
- Rocking chair
- Large picture books
- Indoor gardening equipment
- Fibre optic light tubes
- Projected images for ceilings and walls
- Maracas, bells or other percussion instruments
- Bird sound CDs

Domestic

- Dusters
- Cereal packets
- Other food packets
- Recipes
- Carpet sweepers
- Baking equipment
- Bookshelves
- Cleaning items
- Washing up bowls
- Magazines
- Tea towels
- Paper, envelopes, pens
- Shirts to button
- Socks to pair
- Knots to tie or untie
- Shoe laces
- Knitting needles and wool
- Mops
- Microwaveable cakes or packet desserts
- Wash tubs with sheets or towels to fold
- Serviettes to fold
- Watering can to water plants

Comfort

- Dolls, prams, carrycots
- Soft toys
- Velvet, fur, velour
- Fabrics, curtain samples
- Pictures of pets
- Baby clothes
- Items to 'play' with
- Nursery rhymes
- Teddy bears

Rummaging	Reminiscence	Cognitive
• Chest of drawers – with items spilling out	• Local pictures, maps	• Crafts
• Boxes of handbags	• Old household items	• Quizzes
• Trays of jewellery	• Photo albums	• Games – dominoes, Scrabble etc.
• Coat hooks and coat stands with hanging items	• Old toys	• Old sayings
• Treasure chests	• Baby clothes	• Classic poems
• Wall racks	• Role charts	• Word games
• Collections of hats	• Wedding dresses	• Shopping catalogues
• Dressing up clothes	• Key shops in past	• Travel brochures
• Baskets of objects	• Work items – tools	• Jigsaw puzzles
– Lace, shells, coins, fountain pens.	• Kitchen kit	
• Packaging – boxes, bubble wrap	• Toolbox kit	
	• Sports box	

Movement

- Balls
- Sports – darts, golf, skittles, floor basketball
- Games – Hoopla, ring or bean bag toss, Giant Connect 4
- Basketball net or mini putting game in garden
- Balloons
- Scarves for dancing
- Punch clown
- Parachute
- Large lycra sheets
- Sensory elastic circle
- Spinning tops

Musical

- Instruments
- Headphones
- Good range of well labelled CDs
- Posters – old songs – performers
- Dance music
- Karaoke style CDs with words on screen to prompt singing

Spiritual

- Designated quiet space
- Prayer and hymn books
- Religious artefacts
- Pictures – art, clouds, waves, animals, birdsong
- Organ music
- Gospel music

The Arts

- Paints/Aqua paints
- Colouring sheets
- Pottery
- Photographs
- Life history albums

Fun

- Puppets
- Hats
- Feather boas
- Hawaiian skirts
- Carnival sticks
- Feather dusters

Work life

- Items to give 'jobs'
- Office area with typewriter, paper, envelopes, stationery items
- Cleaning materials
- Things which screw and fit together
- Uniforms – nurses, military etc.

Appendix 3: Developing resources linked to the five senses

SIGHT

- Mobiles for the ceilings or in the line of vision of people who are staring upwards for long periods. Mobiles with crystals to catch the light.

- Some larger pictures for the walls – big images of beautiful gardens or trees or animals – try and link to life stories of people.

- Some food related images for dining room.

- Affordable large wall murals including pretend window views available from internet.

- Hat stands near entrance of lounges with hats and scarves to encourage staff to put these on as they go into a room to be more playful and interactive.

- Fairy lights/LED candles.

- Soap petals which dissolve in the bath.

- Laminated images – old calendars with pictures of places, children, animals, gardens.

- A wide range of DVDs – Try out old fashioned visual comedy DVDs like Laurel and Hardy, classics like Morecambe and Wise, Dad's Army and Are you Being Served or the musicals such as Sound of Music, Oklahoma or My Fair Lady or singers such as Foster and Allen. It is important to check individual taste with these as a 'Carry on' Film, for example, might be one person's idea of fun and another's worst nightmare! DVDs of aquariums or a pretend log fire can also be purchased, which can create a soothing stimulation for the eyes.

- Take time to ensure that people who are lying in one position have a good line of eye vision to see a television screen. In some cases, mounting the television for people who are looking upwards might be important.

- Use YouTube if you have access to the internet. Search for clips from many of the classic songs or comedies or find funny clips of animals and children e.g. Micah the baby boy watching dad ripping paper cannot fail to make people smile!

- Use Google maps to look at a favourite street or someone's home town.

SOUND

- More CD players or an iPod deck and iPod with a wide range of music. Check individual tastes!

- Soft headphones can sometimes be used for individuals to listen to own music in communal areas.

- Musical instruments – maracas, bells, egg shakers etc.

- Laminated song sheets around the room to encourage staff to start singing spontaneously.

- Collections of poetry books, children's verses and limericks, coffee table picture books, story books or short stories like James Herriott vet stories, a book of common prayers, The Friendship Book series have a daily story or thought for the day.

- Portable microphone for story-telling, poetry reading and singing.

- Bird or other animal sounds.

TOUCH

- Microwavable soft cuddly animals (some with lavender or other aromatherapy smells available in chemists and department stores).

- Warm flannels after meals to clean faces and hands as well as provide a sensory experience.

- Boxes of fabrics (different textures and colours) feathers, rope or curtain pulls, balls of wool, ribbons – haberdashery items.

- 'Stress' balls, different texture balls or fun shaped balls (animals, fruits etc.).

- Good collection of massage creams – avoid things which are too sticky and make sure that some sensitive skin options are also available – check any allergy issues.

- Tool box (may be popular with men in particular).

- Boxes of toys for example small toy animals or cars to hold and talk about.

- Objects which evoke memories e.g. sea shells and sand, a military uniform.

TASTE

- Fruit smoothies.
- Wide range of flavour juices and yoghurts (passion fruit, elderflower etc.).
- Hot chocolates.
- Ice-creams.
- Soft crisps – Wotsits.
- Marshmallows.
- Fresh fruit chopped up.
- Hot pastries.
- Cakes.
- Chocolate fountain to dip food in.
- A Bar with alcoholic and non-alcoholic drinks.
- Taste sessions – cheeses, teas, cocktails.

SMELL

- Fresh flowers.
- Chopped herbs.
- Coffee machine.
- Bread maker.
- Fry up some onion, butter and potato or bacon for breakfast smells.
- Plug-in air fresheners or oil diffusers (seek specialist guidance).
- Some perfume bottles with a variety of pretty shapes and assorted scents.
- Smells which evoke memories e.g. shoe polish, baby powder.

NB: Individual risk assessment will be needed to ensure that all of the above items can be safely used. When assessing risks, always think about the benefits to the person's wellbeing as well as any potential hazards involved.

Appendix 4: Simple activities which can be done in less than a minute

- SMILE!
- Say hello – greet someone by name.
- Give a hug or kiss.
- Shake hands/salute.
- 'Give me five' – hands clap.
- Tell a joke.
- Recite a poem.
- Sing a song.
- Give a compliment/notice appearance.
- Talk about the weather.
- Do a little dance.
- Wink or wave or do a thumbs up sign.
- Share some fruit – e.g. open a Satsuma and give half to another person.
- Talk about accessories – a bag, a scarf, earrings.
- Wear something funny.
- Put on a hat.
- Smell a cream, a soap, some perfume.
- Give a hand massage.
- Put on some lipstick.
- Offer a flower to touch or smell.
- Pick up an object to look at and touch.
- Read from a book or magazine.
- Offer a cushion or a rug – make someone comfortable.
- Hold hands.
- Share a hot drink.
- Offer a sweet, biscuit, treat.
- Blow bubbles.
- Chink glasses of drink together and say 'Cheers'.
- Discuss daily news.
- Open curtains and discuss view/weather.
- Share a bit of gossip or personal news from your own life.
- Share a photograph.
- Do 'stone, paper, scissors', 'one potato, two potato… ', 'pat-a-cake'
- Ask someone's opinion or advice.
- Look at fish or brush or stroke a pet.
- Open a musical box or turn on an electronic moving or singing toy.
- Walk/skip/dance arm in arm.
- Brush hair.
- Act 'daft' – silly face, trip up etc.
- Say 'Bless you' when someone sneezes.

Appendix 5: List of contributors

A particularly big thank you for the wonderful photographs in this book which bring each 'essence' to life, provided by:

Wisteria House Care Home, Stoke, Plymouth

Moorehall Lodge, Moorehall Healthcare, Ardee, Ireland

Deerhurst Nursing Home, Brunelcare, Bristol

Wren Hall Nursing Home, Selston, Nottinghamshire

Etheldred House Care Centre, Excelcare, Cambridge

Coombe House Residential Home, Liskeard, Cornwall

Dan Y Mynydd Care Home, Porth, Rhondda Cynon Taf

Leonard Elms Care Home, Congresbury, Somerset

Spring Lodge, Kingsley Healthcare, Woolverstone, Suffolk

Landermeads Nursing Home, Chilwell, Nottingham

Ilford Park Polish Home, Stover, Newton Abbot

Colin Allinson photography, Etheldred House Care Centre

Kate Hanton, Canada

Thanks to the following care homes and individuals for their quotes, stories and other contributions:

Anita Astle, Wren Hall Nursing Home, Selston, Nottinghamshire

Aine Boswarthack, Oakfield Nursing Home

Eve Carder, Landermeads Nursing Home, Chilwell, Nottingham

Dan y Mynydd Care Home, Porth, Rhondda Cynon Taf

Alex Graybow, Dramatherapist working in London and Essex

George Hythe House and Holmfield Day Centre, Leicester

Lesley Hobbs, Deerhurst Care Home, Brunelcare, Bristol

Santall Horn, Etheldred House Care Centre, Excelcare, Cambridge

Anita Moran, Pendine Park, Wrexham

Mountpleasant Lodge, FirstCare, Kilcock, Co.Kildare, Ireland

Jacki Perry and Monarch Healthcare – Parkside, Nottinghamshire and Haddon House, Derbyshire, Nursing Homes

Mary Phelan, Baltinglass District Hospital, Co. Wicklow, Ireland

Shaw healthcare – Elizabeth House, Froome Bank, Hawthorns and Rotherlea Care Homes

Thanks to Eve Carder, Deputy CEO and Senior Consultant Nurse, Dementia Care Matters and formerly Senior Manager at Landermeads Nursing Home for her assistance in writing the Essence of the Day chapter.

Appendix 6: References

Sheard, D (2013) Steering culture change matters in dementia care home

Perrin, T (1997) 'The puzzling, provocative question of play', Journal of Dementia Care 5, 2, 15–17

Perrin, T and May, H (2000) Wellbeing in Dementia: An Occupational Approach for Therapists and Carers, Churchill Livingstone

Knocker, S (2002) 'Play and metaphor in dementia care and dramatherapy', Journal of Dementia Care, 10, 2, 33–37

Killick, J (2013) Playfulness and Dementia – A Practice Guide, Jessica Kingsley Publishers

Knocker, S (2010) In J. Gilliard and M. Marshall (eds) Time for Dementia, Hawker Publications

Feil, N and De Clerk-Rubin, V (2012) The Validation Breakthrough – Simple Techniques for Communicating with People with Alzheimer's and Other Dementias, Health Professions Press

Pool, J, (2012) The Pool Activity Level (PAL) Instrument for Occupational Profiling, 4th Edition, Jessica Kingsley Publishers

Sheard, D (2011) Achieving – Real outcomes in dementia care homes, Dementia Care Matters

Sheard, D (2013) Accepting that homes have front doors while institutions have 'units' in 'Not another care handbook – pearls of wisdom for care staff', Hawker Publications

NAPA (2010) Activity at the Heart of Care? Activity Toolkit – series of guides including 'Activity Ideas', NAPA

Zoutewelle-Morris, S (2011) Chocolate Rain – 100 Ideas for a Creative Approach to Activities in Dementia Care, Hawker Publications

Bowden and Lewthwaite (2009) The Activity Year Book – A Week by Week Guide for Use in Elderly day and Residential Care, Jessica Kingsley Publishers

NAPA (2010) Everybody's Job – a guide for the whole staff team, NAPA

Bell, V et al (2004) The Best Friends Book of Alzheimer's Activities, Health Professions Press

Appendix 7: Further reading

Alzheimer's Society (2013) Taking part – Activities for people with dementia

Aguirre, E, Spector, A, Streater, A, Hoe, J, Woods, B and Orrell, M (2012) Making a difference 2 – An evidence-based group programme to offer cognitive stimulation therapy to people with dementia, Hawker Publications

Bell, V et al (2004) The Best Friends Book of Alzheimer's Activities, Health Professions Press

Bowden and Lewthwaite (2009) The Activity Year Book – A Week by Week Guide for Use in Elderly Day and Residential Care, Jessica Kingsley Publishers

Crockett, S (2013) Activities for Older People in Care Homes, Jessica Kingsley Publishers

Donaghy, I (2014) Dear Dementia – The Laughter and the Tears, Hawker Publications

Feil, N and De Clerk-Rubin, V (2012) The Validation Breakthrough – Simple Techniques for Communicating with People with Alzheimer's and Other Dementias, Health Professions Press

Killick, J (2013) Playfulness and Dementia – A Practice Guide, Jessica Kingsley Publishers

Killick, J and Craig, C (2012) Creativity and Communication in Persons with Dementia – A Practical Guide

Knocker, S (2013) Home from home. *Nursing Standard.* 27 (22) 20–21

Knocker, S (2014) Achieving culture change in dementia care homes: is training the answer? *The Modern Registered Manager.* 2 (1) 8–12

Marshall, K (2013) Puppetry in Dementia Care, Jessica Kingsley Publishers

Mahoney, F and Hannigan, C (2012) I Can Make a Difference – Creative Caring for People with Dementia, Care for mum Creative Books

NAPA (2010) Activity at the Heart of Care? Activity Toolkit – series of guides including 'Activity Ideas', NAPA

Pool, J, (2012) The Pool Activity Level (PAL) Instrument for Occupational Profiling, 4th Edition, Jessica Kingsley Publishers

Sheard, D (2007) Being – an approach to life and dementia, Alzheimer's Society

Sheard, D (2008) Enabling – quality of life – an evaluation tool, Alzheimer's Society

Sheard, D (2008) Inspiring – leadership mattering in dementia care, Alzheimer's Society

Sheard, D (2008) Growing – training that works in dementia care

Sheard, D (2009) Nurturing – our emotions at work in dementia care, Alzheimer's Society

Sheard, D (2011) Achieving – real outcomes in dementia care homes, Dementia Care Matters Ltd

Sheard, D (2013) Implementing person centred theories in dementia care: exploring the Butterfly approach. *The Modern Registered Manager.* 1 (3) 9–12

Sheard, D (2013) The feeling of 'mattering': the positioning of emotions in dementia care. *The Journal of Dementia Care.* 21 (2) 23–27

Sheard, D (2013) Accepting that homes have front doors while institutions have 'units'. *Not another care handbook.* Hawker Publications. 86–87

Sheard, D (2014) Achieving culture change: a whole organisation approach. *Nursing and Residential Care Journal.* 16 (6) 2–5

Spector, A, Thorgrimsen, L, Woods, B and Orrell, M (2011) Making a difference – the manual for group leaders, Hawker Publications

Tanner, L (2014) Touch – a much misunderstood aspect of care. *Caring Times.* February 2014. 20

Zoutewelle-Morris, S (2011) Chocolate Rain – 100 Ideas for a Creative Approach to Activities in Dementia Care, Hawker Publications

Appendix 8: Useful organisations

Alzheimer's Society
T: 020 7423 3500
www.alzheimers.org.uk

Alive! Activities
Championing activities, reminiscence and life story work for older people
T: 0117 377 4756
www.aliveactivities.org and www.memoryappsfordementia.org.uk

Dementia Care Matters
T: 01273 242335
www.dementiacarematters.com

Hawker Publications
T: 020 7720 2108 x211
www.hawkerpublications.com

JABADAO
Resources and courses for movement based play
T: 01473 328330
info@jabadao.org
www.jabadao.org

NAPA
National Activity Providers Association – supporting care staff to enable older people to live life the way they choose, with meaning and purpose, through information, resources and training
T: 0207 078 9375
www.napa-activities.co.uk

Pictures to Share C.I.C.
Specialist publisher of illustrated books suitable for people with dementia, as well as a free educational book for carers, 'Too Late to Learn to Drive; Dementia, visual perception and the meaning of pictures.'
T: 01829 770024
www.picturestoshare.co.uk

SCIE

Social Care Institute for Excellence – Dementia Gateway Keeping Active and Occupied Section
http://www.scie.org.uk/publications/dementia/living-with-dementia/keeping-active/

Sonas apc

Activating potential for communication using multi-sensory stimulation
T: +353 (0)1 260 8138
www.sonasapc.ie

Validation Therapy

www.vfvalidation.org

The following companies provide a wide range of resources including books, games, sensory and reminiscence items and music:

Activities to Share – www.activitiestoshare.co.uk

The Consortium Care – www.theconsortiumcare.co.uk/activities

Jabadao – www.jabadao.org

Speechmark Publishing – www.speechmark.net